THE TEN VIRGINS

TEN WOMEN, TEN STORIES, TEN LESSONS FOR OUR DAY

EMILY FREEMAN

WITH PAINTINGS BY

SIMON DEWEY

DESERET
BOOK

SALT LAKE CITY, UTAH

Text © 2006 Emily O. Freeman
Illustrations © 2006 Simon Dewey

Visit us at deseretbook.com

Library of Congress Cataloging-in-Publication Data

Freeman, Emily, 1969-
   The ten virgins / Emily Freeman; illustrated by Simon Dewey.
      p. cm.
   Includes bibliographical references.
   ISBN-10 1-59038-622-1 (hardbound: alk. paper)
   ISBN-13 978-1-59038-622-4 (hardbound: alk. paper)
   1. Ten virgins (Parable)—Meditations. I. Dewey, Simon. II. Title.
   BT378.T4F74 2006
   226.8'06—dc22   2006010441

Printed in the United States of America
Publishers Printing, Salt Lake City, UT

10 9 8 7 6 5 4

For

GREG, WHO IS MY LOVE,

CALEB, WHO IS MY WISE ONE,

JOSH, WHO IS MY STRENGTH,

MEG, WHO IS MY JOY, AND

GRACE, WHO IS MY MIRACLE

—EF

INTRODUCTION

Concerning the parable of the Ten Virgins, President Spencer W. Kimball wisely taught:

"I believe that the Ten Virgins represent the people of the Church of Jesus Christ and not the rank and file of the world. All of the virgins, wise and foolish, had accepted the invitation to the wedding supper; they had knowledge of the program and had been warned of the important day to come. They were not the gentiles or the heathens or the pagans, nor were they necessarily corrupt and reprobate, but they were knowing people who were foolishly unprepared for the vital happenings that were to affect their eternal lives.

"They had the saving, exalting gospel, but it had not been made the center of their lives. They knew the way but gave only a small measure of loyalty and devotion. . . .

"Rushing for their lamps to light their way through the blackness, half of them found them empty. They had cheated themselves. They were fools, these five unprepared virgins. Apparently, the bridegroom had tarried for reasons that were sufficient and good. Time had passed, and he had not come. They had heard of his coming for so long, so many times, that the statement seemingly became meaningless to them. Would he ever come? So long had it been since they began expecting him that they were rationalizing that he would never appear. Perhaps it was a myth.

"Hundreds of thousands of us today are in this position. Confidence has been dulled and patience worn thin. It is so hard to wait and be prepared always. But we cannot allow ourselves to slumber. The Lord has given us this parable as a special warning. . . .

"At midnight! Precisely at the darkest hour, when least expected, the bridegroom came. When the world is full of tribulation and help is needed, but it seems the time must be past and hope is vain, then Christ will come. . . . But when the cry sounds, there is no time for preparation. . . . In the daytime, wise and unwise seemed alike; midnight is the time of test and judgment—and of offered gladness" (*Faith Precedes the Miracle* [Salt Lake City: Deseret Book, 1972], 253–55).

In the years that I have studied this parable I have often wondered about the characteristics of the ten virgins. I feel certain that each of them wrestled with many of the same issues that complicate our lives today. I have found myself wishing that the parable would have included a description of these women individually, including what their struggles were and what motivated them to make the choices they made.

Although fictional, these women have become real to me. Over time I have come to understand why they might have made the choices they did. Interestingly, I find a part of myself interwoven into each of the virgins, wise and foolish alike.

I have always believed that each of the ten virgins was

a good woman. The parable teaches that each of them showed wisdom up to a certain point; each accepted the invitation to the wedding, each knew to bring a lamp, and each arrived at the place of celebration on time. However, long before the moment of decision, five of the virgins behaved carelessly, foolishly thinking they had plenty of time to prepare. By the same token, long before the moment of decision, five of the virgins had been preparing for the celebration "at all times and in all things, and in all places" (Mosiah 18:9).

Years of research have led me to believe that there are many virtues that a wise virgin could have. However, there are ten that stand out to me. I have assigned one of these positive qualities to each virgin in this story. Each woman has the agency to choose whether to live the virtue or to live the opposite of the virtue. In the end those choices determine whether or not that woman is wise or foolish.

I hope this story will motivate you and lift your spirit and prompt you to reflect on your relationship with Jesus Christ. I pray that you might truly accept His invitation to "Watch and be ready," looking forward with great anticipation to the celebration ahead.

May you always have enough oil for your lamp.

*N*estled in a grove of trees at the top of a steep hill there was a shop. And every person who toiled up the path to the top came for the same reason: to buy oil.

The shopkeeper was a young man with thick brown hair. His large hands were strong but gentle. He spent much of his time sitting at a wooden workbench, carefully creating small oil lamps. It was his tradition to give one of these lamps to every person who moved into the village. Each lamp was meticulously crafted, and each was different from the others.

Some of them were round, others were oval.

Some were made of ordinary clays, and others were made of terra cotta.

Some were perfectly smooth, while others had intricate designs tooled into their surfaces.

But all of them held oil, and all of them produced light.

The shopkeeper reminded each villager who received a lamp to return to his shop often. The tiny flame the lamp produced could not be maintained without an ongoing supply of oil, and the lamp maker's shop was the only source of oil in the village.

But the path to the top of the hill was steep, and the journey took time and effort.

Those seeking oil would arrive at the lamp maker's shop at all times of the day or night, and each was met with a warm welcome, no matter the hour. The shopkeeper's brown eyes would light up as the lamp owner came through his door, and he would always set his work aside to visit.

Eliana

(HEBREW) "GOD HAS ANSWERED"

One of the first villagers to receive a lamp from the shopkeeper was Eliana, an old woman with gray, braided hair and clear, blue eyes.

Her lamp was molded from pale yellow clay and hardened by firing in the kiln for long hours.

This process had made it possible for her lamp to endure years of use.

By day, Eliana's lamp lit up the shadowed corners of her small home. By night, she sat next to the soft glow and read passages from her most treasured books.

As the evening deepened, she would set her book down beside the lamp on the small table next to her chair. Then, after wrapping a soft blanket around her frail shoulders, she would watch the flame flicker and dance beside her.

On those occasions she would reflect on the moments when the lamp had seen her through joy and celebration and the times when it had given her comfort through disappointment and discouragement.

The lamp's constant light had guided her through change and brought courage in the hours of darkness.

It warmed her heart to realize that even now, after years of use, the flame still burned as brightly as it had the day the lamp was made.

Leora

(H E B R E W) " L I G H T "

After the shopkeeper gave Leora her lamp he had watched her take the hands of other villagers and by its light lead them through the darkness.

He noticed that every time the pathway met another, she would pause, lift her lamp in front of her, and consider her direction.

Because it was hard for her to focus in the darkness, the shopkeeper worried that she might become lost when she came to a fork or a bend in the road. He knew that without enough light, she would not be able to find her way.

So one afternoon he sawed a long branch from a tree outside his shop and whittled it until it was smooth.

Then he crafted a small cup, just large enough for her lamp to fit inside, and fastened it to the end of the long wooden pole.

The shopkeeper knew that Leora would treasure this unique gift.

When evening came, he would sit on his porch high on the hill and watch with satisfaction as she would light her lamp and fit it into the cup on the top of her wooden pole.

She held the lamp high, and it illuminated the entire path before her.

Then she walked through the village streets, helping the lost, the weary, and the worn find their ways home.

Ashira

(HEBREW) "WEALTHY"

The shopkeeper worried for Ashira because she was so rushed and hurried. He knew of her great responsibility as a teacher, healer, mender, and caregiver, but he also knew the concerns of her heart.

On one hand, she was everything to everyone.

On the other hand, she felt like she never got anything accomplished.

Most days it was all she could do to get herself dressed in the morning. As soon as the sun came up over the mountain, she would tuck her long brown hair behind her ears and get right to work.

Sometimes she would pause at the window of her tiny home and look up at the shop on the hill. *Today will be the day*, she would think to herself, between doing the dishes, scrubbing the floor, reading to the children in the village, and the trip to the market. *I will find time*.

The shopkeeper watched her run in and out of her house all day long.

Half the time she had to run back for her shoes.

Most of the time she forgot her lamp.

Gabriella

(HEBREW) "GOD IS MY STRENGTH"

The shopkeeper watched Gabriella closely for many days before he finally came up with the perfect design for her lamp. She was an unassuming woman and rarely called attention to herself, which made the task more challenging.

Her clothing was unadorned but beautiful in its simplicity. She had a natural elegance and an unassuming style that was all her own.

She was also gentle and wise beyond her years. Those who stopped at her home to visit found a loyal friend at the welcoming door, one who always spoke of others with respect and admiration.

After much thought, the shopkeeper molded the clay for her lamp into an oval that fit perfectly in the palm of her small hand. With painstaking care, he smoothed away each rough spot and imperfection.

Gabriella's lamp was simple, but lovely.

Its understated beauty allowed onlookers to focus on the flame.

Adi

Adi wondered if she would ever be enough, and the shopkeeper watched her struggle.

She felt that she was so much less than others—her dark hair straight and plain, her eyes simply brown.

He had crafted her lamp with a complicated geometric design, one that would stand out.

Still, Adi spent much of her time comparing it to the lamps he had given the others. In some ways she felt that her lamp was beautiful, but in others that it was greatly lacking.

She was constantly looking for ways to modify the gift she had been given.

The shopkeeper knew that she would quickly tire of her lamp, so he hid a yellow diamond pattern in the intricate design of the brown clay.

With use, the diamond design would eventually show through.

Uncomprehending, Adi searched for happiness, never discovering the hidden treasure that she already carried with her.

Malka

(HEBREW) "QUEEN"

Malka's lamp was hewn from a beautiful piece of soft red sandstone.

The large end of the lamp was a perfect circle that angled into a small triangle where the wick was trimmed.

The design was unique and had taken the shopkeeper hours to shape and smooth.

Malka had thanked the shopkeeper for the gift and placed it carefully in her bag. She was young and strong. She kept her dark hair swept up in a tight bun, which accentuated her beautiful, black, piercing eyes and the defined features of her face.

Sometimes she would look at her lamp in wonder. She was flattered that the shopkeeper had taken the time to make her such a beautiful gift.

But she was still so young, and none of her friends ever used their lamps. Besides, Malka knew the village so well that she didn't need a light to guide her way.

She rarely lit her lamp.

She could see fine through the darkness.

So she set the exquisite lamp out in her home as a decoration for all the villagers to admire.

Dina

(HEBREW) "GENTLE"

Dina had been the first to ask the shopkeeper for a vessel to hold more oil. It seemed that the supply in her lamp was not enough to keep the flame burning between her frequent visits to the shop.

She used her lamp to light the way when she traveled to the homes of the villagers during the darkest hours of the night.

It had stood vigil with the sick and had warmed the lives of the lonely.

Dina was known throughout the village for her ability to bring comfort at any time of the day or night. She had seen sorrow and she knew grief.

The shopkeeper often watched Dina as she walked through the streets of the tiny village, sharing her simple abundance with those who had little.

She used her lamp constantly and often worried that she might run out of oil on her journeys through the darkness. And so the shopkeeper crafted her a terra cotta vessel to carry extra oil for her lamp.

Nava

(H E B R E W) " B E A U T I F U L "

Nava's lamp was molded from beautiful deep-orange clay. After carefully inscribing an intricate floral design across the top of the lamp, the shopkeeper had gently placed it in the kiln.

As Nava walked home with her lamp, the dancing flame illuminated her hazel eyes and the soft curls of her auburn hair. She watched the flame flicker and knew the gift was something to be treasured.

However, keeping the flame lit was a difficult task, one that required diligence and constant attention.

And so, even though Nava carried it with her wherever she went, she rarely lit her lamp.

On special occasions Nava would sit down at the table in her kitchen and carefully pull the wick through the small hole at the top of the lamp.

Using a sharp knife she would trim the used and blackened portion of the wick before filling the lamp's shallow basin with olive oil.

Admiring the soft, glowing beauty of the flame, she would wonder why she didn't light her lamp more often.

Liraz

(HEBREW) "I HAVE A SECRET"

Liraz had a hard time waiting for her lamp to be made.

Often she would run into the shop, pulling her windblown hair back into place, her round, brown eyes wide with anticipation.

She visited the shopkeeper every day as he sat at his wooden workbench, molding her lamp. She could scarcely wait for the moment when it would be done.

He appreciated her company and enjoyed their conversations.

After the lamp was finished, the visits became fewer and farther between. It seemed the journey up the hill took too long.

In the morning she was too busy. In the evening she was too tired.

Only when she was in desperate need would she come.

And on those days the shopkeeper was grateful for the visit.

Jessa

(HEBREW) "GRACE"

Jessa wasn't sure how it had happened. She woke up one morning to find her lamp broken in pieces on the floor. Perhaps it had blown off the table during the furious winds that had preceded the storm.

She was devastated.

Sobbing, she picked up each of the pieces and set them gently back on the table. Every time she walked past the small pile she closed her eyes and wondered if the heartache she felt inside would ever go away.

After many days she finally accepted what she had known all along: There was only one who could fix the lamp.

Fighting back tears, she gathered up the broken pieces and started up the hill.

It wasn't long before it began to rain. The path became slippery, and then the downpour came. The wind whipped her wet, brown hair into her dark eyes, and it became hard to see. Realizing she wasn't going to make it, Jessa cried out for help.

Within an instant he was there.

The shopkeeper had been walking just below her. He covered the young woman with his heavy, warm cloak. Then he lifted her into his strong and steady arms and carried her up the hill.

After the storm, he sent Jessa down the hill with two gifts—her restored lamp and a grateful heart.

The shopkeeper knew that each of the women used her
lamp in her own way.
He also knew that those who visited his shop most
frequently were those who used their lamps most often.
As he was asked to do so, the shopkeeper
would refill their tiny lamps with oil, drop by drop,
according to each woman's need.

In time, the shopkeeper decided to
marry and chose a bride.

Each of the ten women received an
invitation to attend the wedding, and each
was asked to take part in one of the village's
most honored customs.

On the night of the wedding these ten
chosen women would use their lamps to light
the doorway of the home where the wedding
would be held. The glow from their lamps would
bring honor to the groom as he entered the home for
the celebration.

It was a great privilege to be given this invitation—
one that many women waited a lifetime to receive.

Then shall the kingdom of heaven be likened unto ten virgins, which

took their lamps, and went forth to meet the bridegroom. MATTHEW 25:1

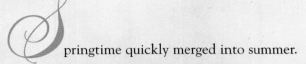

Springtime quickly merged into summer.

The leaves of the fig tree began to shoot forth. The women could barely contain their excitement for the events that were about to unfold.

The long-awaited day finally arrived.

The entire village gathered to celebrate the momentous occasion. Balconies and rooftops were all full. People lined the narrow streets, and those who hoped for a better view climbed up to sit on the garden walls.

Soon the wedding party would pass through these streets as they journeyed to the home where the ceremony would take place.

The villagers danced and sang while they waited. Small children scattered petals of brightly colored flowers through the streets. Young boys handed out candles to the crowd of onlookers.

As the celebration continued, afternoon turned into twilight.

Then, as darkness gathered, one of the villagers began to light the flaming torches that had been placed along the way.

The dancing lights from the candles and the illumination of the torches created an impressive spectacle under the starry stillness of the velvet night.

As preparations continued, anticipation grew, and the ten women made their way through the crowded streets of the village to the entry of the home where the wedding would be held.

And the shopkeeper watched from the top of the hill and waited.

And five of them were wise, and five were foolish.

They that were foolish took their lamps, and took no oil with them: but the wise took oil in their vessels with their lamps. MATTHEW 25:2–4

inally the ten chosen women arrived at their destination. They each found a comfortable place in the alcove of the doorway and settled down to wait.

Time passed slowly and, growing weary, the women closed their eyes and slept.

The eleventh hour came and went. The villagers grew tired of waiting. Perhaps there would not be a wedding after all. Many returned to their homes. Some slumbered in the streets.

The entire village grew quiet under the soft glow of the moon.

And still, the shopkeeper watched from the top of the hill and waited.

Then, at precisely the darkest hour of the night, when a hush had fallen over the sleeping village, those villagers who had patiently waited and watched raised a cry. The silence was broken.

The women awoke with a start.

The moment was at hand!

It was time to trim their lamps.

While the bridegroom tarried, they all slumbered and slept. And at midnight there was a cry made, Behold, the bridegroom cometh; go ye out to meet him. MATTHEW 25:5–6

*S*uddenly alert, Jessa quickly used her extra oil to fill her darkened lamp. A lifetime of waiting had come to an end, and she hoped she had made sufficient preparation.

Gabriella reached for her vessel and filled her simple lamp with all of the remaining oil she had. As she carefully tucked her empty vessel away, Nava, who was sitting beside her, let out a small cry. Her flame had gone out! Her lamp was empty! She had not brought any extra oil.

What would she do now?

She had looked forward to this night for as long as she could remember. She desperately wanted to be a part of the wedding. But looking back, she realized that her preparation for this special occasion hadn't been enough. Now she wondered why she hadn't thought to get extra oil; but with so many things to do, the thought had never crossed her mind.

Frantic, she turned to Gabriella to see if she had extra oil, but there was none to spare.

She watched the other women hastily trimming their lamps as tears ran down her cheeks and fell on the empty flowered lamp that was cradled in the folds of her dress.

Realizing her mistake, Nava fell to the ground, weeping.

Then all those virgins arose, and trimmed their lamps. MATTHEW 25:7

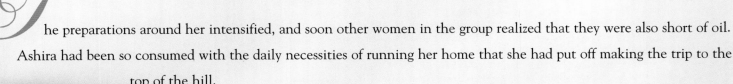

The preparations around her intensified, and soon other women in the group realized that they were also short of oil. Ashira had been so consumed with the daily necessities of running her home that she had put off making the trip to the top of the hill.

Eventually she had run out of time.

Liraz hadn't talked to the shopkeeper for quite a while. The days had turned into months, until she lost track. Although she had anticipated this day for a long time, it hadn't occurred to her that he would arrive so late in the evening.

She had not prepared for the delay.

Malka had wondered if there would really be a wedding. She had considered buying oil for her lamp, but since she rarely used it, she figured it would only go to waste.

Adi had used all of her extra money to buy a new dress for the wedding. She had wanted to impress the others.

There hadn't been enough money left over to buy oil.

Having seldom lit her lamp, Nava just assumed she had enough oil. How could it be all gone?

And the foolish said unto

the wise, Give us of your oil;

for our lamps are gone out.

MATTHEW 25:8

The five women rushed over to Dina and Leora and fell at their feet, begging for help.

These women had brightened the darkness for them in the past. Surely they would share their oil.

But what had been prepared could not be shared in an instant. Every drop was needed now.

They could not risk letting their own lamps run empty.

As much as they longed to help their friends, there was nothing they could do.

Finally, weeping tears of frustration, the five foolish women turned to Eliana.

The wise woman could give them nothing but advice.

"You must go out into the darkness of the night and find oil. Buy what you need and then return. Hurry, he is coming!"

Clutching their empty lamps the frantic women ran out through the garden gate and into the village streets.

They would never make it back in time.

But the wise answered, saying, Not so; lest there be not enough for us and you: but go ye rather to them that sell, and buy for yourselves. MATTHEW 25:9

The five women who remained carefully finished emptying the oil from their vessels into their lamps.

They trimmed their wicks and lit their lamps.

Then each raised her lamp to light the doorway in honor of the groom.

The bridegroom made his way through the crowded streets. He turned the corner just in time to see the five foolish women running toward the hill.

His heart ached as he reflected on their lack of preparation.

And while they went to buy, the bridegroom came; . . .

Then he lifted his eyes to the doorway and took in the sight he had waited a lifetime to see.

Leora was there with her finely crafted pole, holding her lamp high.

The flame from Gabriella's simple lamp lit up her eyes, which glistened with anticipation.

Dina lifted her lamp so the flame could dance with the others, adding a soft glow to the brilliant display of light.

Eliana rested a wrinkled hand on Dina's arm and lifted her yellow lamp as high as her frail arm could reach.

And quiet Jessa had fallen to her knees, her lamp cupped carefully in both hands, while tears of overwhelming gratitude streamed down her cheeks.

. . . and they that

were ready . . .

These five wise women had each come to know the bridegroom, and their hearts filled with joy as they watched him stride through the garden gate and down the pathway that led to the great wooden door.

He had lifted them and strengthened them. When they had been weak, he had made them strong. When they had thought they could not go on, he had made up the difference. When they found disappointment, he had offered consoling peace.

The shopkeeper paused and greeted each of the women one by one. Then he invited them in for the wedding feast. Together the five women raised their lamps in a final tribute and went in with him to the marriage; and the great wooden door was shut.

. . . went in with him to the

marriage: and the door

was shut. MATTHEW 25:10

Watch therefore, for ye know neither the day

nor the hour wherein the Son of man cometh.

MATTHEW 25:13.

Eliana

A WOMAN OF THE SCRIPTURES

"And at that day, when I shall come in my glory, shall the parable be fulfilled which I spake concerning the ten virgins. For they that are wise and have received the truth, . . . and have not been deceived—verily I say unto you, they shall not be hewn down and cast into the fire, but shall abide the day" (D&C 45:56–57).

Leora

A WOMAN WHO TAKES THE SPIRIT FOR HER GUIDE

"Five of the virgins are wise and have taken the Holy Spirit for their guide; their lamps are lighted and they await the coming of Him whose feast it is. But five are foolish; . . . Their lamps are without oil, for they have not made the Holy Ghost their constant companion" (Bruce R. McConkie, *The Millennial Messiah* [Salt Lake City: Deseret Book, 1982], 343).

Ashira

A WOMAN WHO KEEPS THE COMMANDMENTS

"They do not put first in their lives the things of their Lord; other interests consume their attention" (McConkie, *The Millennial Messiah,* 343).

"And so they deemed it not necessary to undertake what must have involved both trouble and carefulness—the bringing their own oil" (Alfred Edersheim, *Life and Times of Jesus the Messiah* [Iowa Falls, Iowa: World Bible Publishers, 1971], 2:457).

Gabriella

A WOMAN WHO RESPECTS SACRED THINGS

"In the oil reserves of the wiser ones we may see the spiritual strength and abundance which diligence and devotion in God's service alone can insure" (James E. Talmage, *Jesus the Christ* [Salt Lake City: Deseret Book, 1983], 537).

"I pray, sisters, that we will rejoice and go on to victory as we prepare for the second coming of our Savior. I pray that we will not be led away by the subtle enticings of the world that sometimes come to us even from those near and dear to us—the enticings that say to us, 'Seek for visibility; seek for power and influence; be sure your own needs are being met.' These are not the teachings of him whose coming we await" (Barbara Winder, "Becoming a Prepared People," *Ensign*, Nov. 1988, 90).

Adi

A WOMAN OF HUMILITY

"Because the daughters of Zion are haughty, and walk with stretched forth necks and wanton eyes, walking and mincing as they go, and making a tinkling with their feet . . . in that day the Lord will take away the bravery of their tinkling ornaments" (Isaiah 3:16, 18).

There was an "entire absence of personal preparation" (Edersheim, *Life and Times of Jesus the Messiah*, 2:457).

Malka

A WOMAN WHO IS LOYAL

"They brought their own lamps, but not their own oil. . . . Probably, not from forgetfulness . . . but from *wilful* neglect, in the belief that [some] would be supplied. . . .

"They had no conception either of *any personal obligation in this matter*, nor that the call would come so suddenly, nor yet that there would be so little interval between the arrival of the Bridegroom and 'the closing of the door'" (Edersheim, *Life and Times of Jesus the Messiah*, 2:456–57; emphasis added).

Dina

A WOMAN OF SERVICE

"Another oil that is not available at midnight is the indispensable oil of home service. This rare oil of service is accumulated through visits to the sick, through lending a helping hand" (Spencer W. Kimball, in *Church News*, May 13, 1995).

Nava

A WOMAN WHO DILIGENTLY PREPARES

There must be "unceasing watchfulness and unwavering diligence in preparation for the coming of the Lord" (Talmage, *Jesus the Christ*, 535).

Liraz

A WOMAN OF PRAYER

"One type of oil is the oil of prayer. It illuminates us and makes us bright and cheery but is difficult to obtain at midnight. One drop or two will not keep the lamp burning long" (Spencer W. Kimball, in *Church News*, May 13, 1995).

"Wherefore, be faithful, praying always, having your lamps trimmed and burning, and oil with you, that you may be ready at the coming of the Bridegroom" (D&C 33:17).

Jessa

A WOMAN OF GRACE, PERSONAL CONVERSION, AND HOLINESS

The wise had "the preparation of grace, personal conversion and holiness. . . . Every one must be personally prepared for meeting the Bridegroom" (Edersheim, *Life and Times of Jesus the Messiah*, 2:457).

REFERENCES

Each lamp was meticulously crafted, and each was different from the others

"The Ten Virgins brought . . . 'their own lamps.' Emphasis must be laid on this. This much was there of *personal* preparation on the part of all" (Edersheim, *Life and Times of Jesus the Messiah*, 2:456; emphasis in original).

The lampmaker's shop was the only source of oil in the village

"The Parable of the Ten Virgins may . . . be thus summarised: Be ye personally prepared; be ye prepared for any length of time; *be ye prepared to go to Him directly*" (Edersheim, *Life and Times of Jesus the Messiah*, 2:453; emphasis added).

She would light her lamp and fit it into the cup on the top of her wooden pole

"Each had her lamp attached to the end of a rod so as to be held aloft in the festal march" (Talmage, *Jesus the Christ*, 536).

"The lamps consisted of a round receptacle for pitch or oil for the wick. This was placed in a hollow cup or deep saucer—the Beth Shiqqua—which was fastened by a pointed end into a long wooden pole, on which it was borne aloft. According to Jewish authorities, it was the custom in the East to carry in a bridal procession about ten such lamps" (Edersheim, *Life and Times of Jesus the Messiah*, 2:455).

Drop by drop according to their need

"Like the small oil lamps of the Middle East, which require a careful and methodical and slow effort to fill, so in our own lives we need to build our reservoirs of faith and spiritual experience gradually and consistently" (Robert L. Millet, *Steadfast and Immovable* [Salt Lake City: Deseret Book, 1992], 33).

Each of the ten women received an invitation to attend the wedding

"In the last days, before the Son of Man comes, his church is likened unto ten virgins, all of whom have accepted the gospel invitation to attend the marriage feast of the Lamb" (McConkie, *The Millennial Messiah*, 343).

"It was the custom . . . to carry in a bridal procession about ten such lamps. . . . Ten was the number required to be present at any office or ceremony" (Edersheim, *Life and Times of Jesus the Messiah*, 2:455).

"Before he arrives, the maidens in waiting come forth with lamps and candles a short distance to light up the entrance, and do honour to the bridegroom and the group of relatives and intimate friends around him. These pass into the final rejoicing of the marriage supper; the others who have discharged their duty in accompanying him to the door, immediately disperse, and the door is shut" (George Mackie, *Bible Manners and Customs* [New York: Fleming H. Revell, 1898], 126).

The leaves of the fig tree began to shoot forth

"Now learn a parable of the fig tree; When his branch is yet tender, and putteth forth leaves, ye know that summer is nigh: So likewise ye, when ye shall see all these things, know that it is near, even at the doors" (Matthew 24:32–33).

And the shopkeeper watched from the top of the hill and waited

"The Bridegroom is not in the town, but somewhere far away; so that it cannot be known at what precise hour He may arrive. But it *is* known that He will come that night" (Edersheim, *Life and Times of Jesus the Messiah*, 2:454; emphasis in original).

At precisely the darkest hour of the night

"It is midnight—when sleep is deepest—when suddenly 'there was a cry, Behold, the Bridegroom cometh!' . . .

"Christ will come when least expected—at midnight—and when the Church, having become accustomed to His long delay, has gone to sleep" (Edersheim, *Life and Times of Jesus the Messiah*, 2:457, 458–59).

Those villagers who had patiently waited and watched raised a cry

"The bridegroom is the centre of interest. . . . From time to time women raise their voices in the peculiar shrill, wavering shriek by which joy is expressed at marriages and other times of family and public rejoicing. The sound is heard at a great distance, and is repeated by other voices in advance of the procession, and thus intimation is given of the approach half an hour or more before the marriage escort arrives. . . . Along the route the throng becomes more dense, and begins to move with the retinue bearing lights. As the house is approached the excitement increases, the bridegroom's pace is quickened, and the alarm is raised in louder tones and more repeatedly, 'He is coming, he is coming!'" (Mackie, *Bible Manners and Customs*, 124–26).

She reached for her vessel

"But of the ten virgins five had wisely carried an extra supply of oil, while the other five, probably counting on no great delay, or assuming that they would be able to borrow from others, or perchance having negligently given no thought at all to the matter, had no oil except the one filling with which their lamps had been supplied at starting" (Talmage, *Jesus the Christ*, 536).

What had been prepared could not be shared in an instant

"Spiritual preparedness cannot be shared in an instant because we each fill our lamps drop by drop in our daily living," (James E. Faust, "Your Light—a Standard to All Nations," *Ensign*, May 2006, 113).

"The refusal of the wise virgins to give of their oil at such a critical time must not be regarded as uncharitable; the circumstance typifies the fact that in the day of judgment every soul must answer for himself; there is no way by which the righteousness of one can be credited to another's account" (Talmage, *Jesus the Christ*, 537).

The wise woman could give them nothing but advice

"Instead of oil they could impart only advice to their unfortunate sisters, whom they directed to go to the nearest shop and buy for themselves" (Talmage, *Jesus the Christ*, 536).

Then they each raised her lamp to light the doorway in honor of the groom

"The lighted lamp, which each of the maidens carried, is the outward profession of Christian belief and practice" (Talmage, *Jesus the Christ*, 537).

And the great wooden door was shut

"His Coming will be far on in the night; it will be sudden; it will be rapid: be prepared therefore, be ever and personally prepared! . . . So rapid will be the end, that, ere the foolish Virgins can return, the door has been forever closed. . . . Lastly, we are to learn, . . . that it is impossible in the day of Christ's Coming to make up for neglect of previous preparation, and that those who have failed to meet Him, even though of the bridal Virgins, shall be finally excluded for being strangers to the Bridegroom" (Edersheim, *Life and Times of Jesus the Messiah*, 2:458–59).